# MY CABBAGE PATCH KID AND ME™

# MY CABBAGE PATCH KID AND ME™

## A record of everything that happens to us

**QuillMark II**™

Random House, Inc.
New York, New York

# My name:

_____

# My Cabbage Patch Kid's name:

_____

# The day my Cabbage Patch Kid came to live with me:

## Date:

# My Cabbage Patch Kid was given to me by:

_____

# Here is what my Cabbage Patch Kid looked like on that day:

# We live at this address:

_____

_____

# Here is a picture by me of where we live:

# These are the people we live with:

_____

_____

_____

_____

_____

_____

_____

_____

_____

_____

# My Cabbage Patch Kid's birth certificate:

# My Cabbage Patch Kid's validated adoption papers:

# Important Birthdays

## My birthday:

_____

## My Cabbage Patch Kid's birthday:

_____

# Friends' birthdays:

_____

_____

_____

_____

_____

# Relatives' birthdays:

_____

_____

_____

_____

_____

# Other special days:

# Here are more things to know about my Cabbage Patch Kid and me:

My height:

_____

My Cabbage Patch Kid's height:

_____

## My weight:

_____

## My Cabbage Patch Kid's weight:

_____

# The color of my eyes:

_____

## The color of my Cabbage Patch Kid's eyes:

_____

# My hair color:

_____

# My Cabbage Patch Kid's hair color:

_____

# Here is an outline of my hand:

# Here is an outline of my Cabbage Patch Kid's hand:

# Here is an outline of my foot:

# Here is an outline of my Cabbage Patch Kid's foot:

# This is what I look like:
## (drawing or photo)

# This is what my Cabbage Patch Kid looks like:

# What I like to do best:

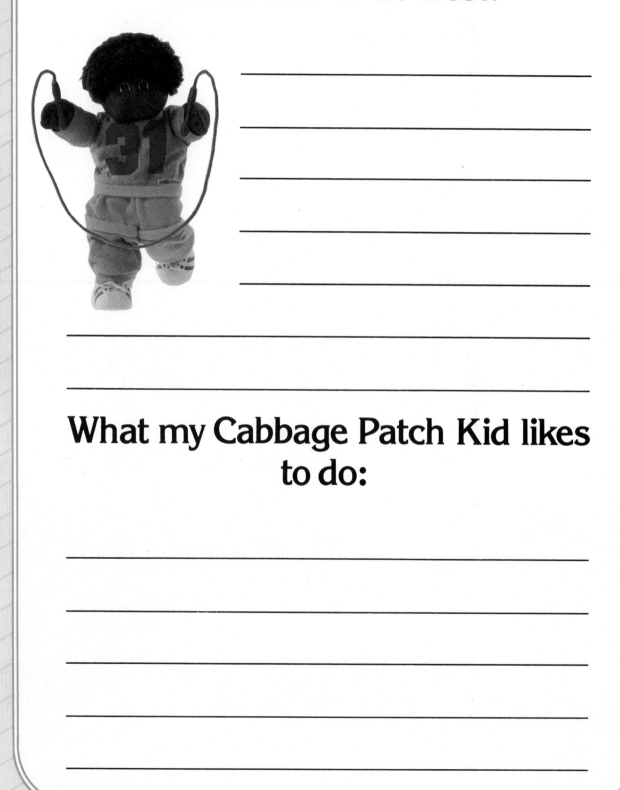

_____

_____

_____

_____

_____

_____

_____

# What my Cabbage Patch Kid likes to do:

_____

_____

_____

_____

_____

# One thing I don't like to do:

_____

_____

_____

_____

_____

# One thing my Cabbage Patch Kid doesn't like to do:

_____

_____

_____

_____

_____

# My Favorite Things

## Food:

_____

_____

_____

_____

_____

_____

## Books:

_____

_____

_____

_____

_____

_____

# Movies:

_____

_____

_____

_____

_____

# Sports:

_____

_____

_____

_____

_____

_____

# My Favorite Things

## Girls' names:

_____

_____

_____

_____

## Boys' names:

_____

_____

_____

_____

# Colors:

_____

_____

_____

_____

# Animals/pets:

_____

_____

_____

_____

# My Favorite Things

## TV shows:

_____

_____

_____

_____

## Toys:

_____

_____

_____

_____

_____

# Games:

_____

_____

_____

_____

_____

# Holidays:

_____

_____

_____

_____

_____

# This is what my Cabbage Patch Kid does during the day:

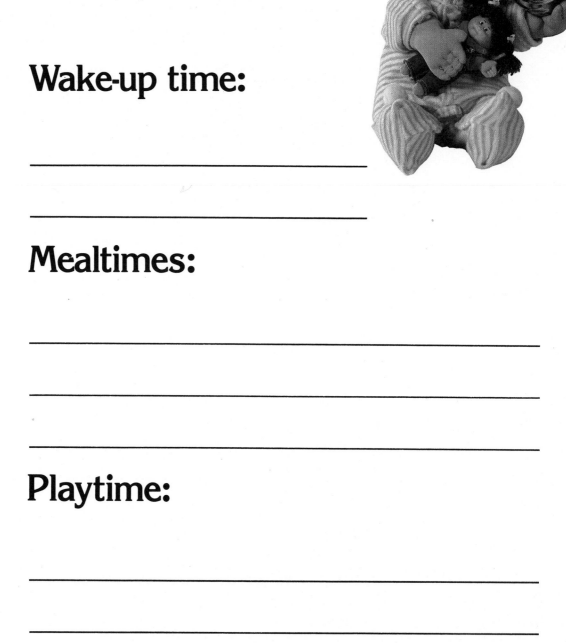

## Wake-up time:

_____

_____

## Mealtimes:

_____

_____

_____

## Playtime:

_____

_____

_____

# Storytime:

_____

_____

_____

# Bedtime:

_____

_____

_____

# My best friend's name is:

_____

_____

# Here is a picture of my best friend:

# Things my friend and I like to do:

_____

_____

_____

_____

_____

# School Days

## Favorite teacher:

_____

## Favorite subject:

_____

# Least favorite subject:

_____

# My classmates:

_____

_____

_____

_____

_____

_____

_____

_____

_____

# Travel Log

Here is a record of a trip my Cabbage Patch Kid and I took:

When we went:

_____

_____

Where we went:

_____

_____

Whom we went with:

_____

_____

# How we traveled:

_____

_____

# How long it took:

_____

_____

# Where we stayed:

_____

_____

# What we ate:

_____

_____

# The things I liked best about our trip:

_____

_____

_____

_____

_____

_____

_____

# Here is a picture of something interesting I saw on my trip:

# Some other places my Cabbage Patch Kid and I have been:

_____

_____

# Some places I would like to go:

_____

_____

_____

_____

_____

_____

# Here is a map I drew of my town:

(label where you live, the library, the school, the supermarket, place of worship, where your friends live, and any other important places):

# Things I like about winter:

_____

_____

# My Cabbage Patch Kid likes:

_____

_____

# Things I like about spring:

_____

_____

# My Cabbage Patch Kid likes:

_____

_____

# Things I like about summer:

_____

_____

# My Cabbage Patch Kid likes:

_____

_____

# Things I like about autumn:

_____

_____

# My Cabbage Patch Kid likes:

_____

_____

# When I grow up, I want to be:

_____

_____

_____

_____

_____

_____

_____

# My Cabbage Patch Kid wants to be:

_____

_____

_____

_____

_____

_____

_____

# Here is a story about my Cabbage Patch Kid and me:

_____

_____

_____

_____

_____

_____

_____

_____

_____

_____

5